# Prince of L

## A Play in One Act

## Michael Lesslie

A SAMUEL FRENCH ACTING EDITION

FOUNDED 1830

SAMUELFRENCH.COM
SAMUELFRENCH-LONDON.CO.UK

## PRINCE OF DENMARK

Commissioned by the National Theatre Discover Programme and first presented in the Cottesloe auditorium of the National Theatre, London in October 2010 with the following cast:

| | |
|---|---|
| **Laertes** | Chris Levens |
| **Reynaldo** | James Williams |
| **Osric** | Abubakar Salim |
| **Ophelia** | Eve Ponsonby |
| **Hamlet** | Calum Finlay |
| **Rosencrantz** | Oliver Yellop |
| **Guildenstern** | Adrian Chisholm |
| **Horatio** | Joseph Sarrington Smith |
| **Player** | Kaffe Keating-Jungreuthmayer |
| **Marcellus** | Paul Andrew |
| **Ensemble** | James Flude, Adam Jones, Theo Morton, Hamish Riddle, Nicholas Sheedy, Lawrence Swaddle |

Directed by Anthony Banks

## CHARACTERS

All the characters are in their late teens and can be played by either male or female actors.

**Laertes**
**Reynaldo**
**Osric**
**Ophelia**
**Hamlet**
**Rosencrantz**
**Guildenstern**
**Horatio**
**Player**
**Marcellus**
**Several Courtiers**
**Several Guards**
**Several Players**

## SYNOPSIS OF SCENES

The action of the play takes place in various locations in Elsinore in the same temporal and political setting as Shakespeare's *Hamlet*, medieval Denmark focalized through Elizabethan England

# INTRODUCTION

Michael Lesslie played Hamlet when he was at school so I knew he'd be able to get his head inside the younger prince and present his story in a way which resonated with contemporary teenagers. The story he has created stands completely apart from Shakespeare's play though it enthusiastically borrows characters, riffs on themes and reverberates with the rotten state in a way which will be intriguing both for those who haven't yet experienced Hamlet and also those who have.

Prince of Denmark presents a whole generation of teenage characters we rarely see in historical plays about royal families. Apathetic and broody, they loll around Elsinore castle, killing time by play-fighting with each other. The swagger and poise of their ambition in the late 1500s is not dissimilar to a certain breed of young men who hunger for power and aspire to run the universe half a millennium later.

**Anthony Banks, October 2010**

*Anthony Banks directed the first production of Prince of Denmark at the National Theatre in October 2010.*

## AUTHOR'S NOTE

When Anthony suggested writing a prequel to *Hamlet* using only the young characters, I hesitated: trying to add anything to so monumental a text seemed presumptuous, and the idea of plugging gaps in a plot invigorated by its ambiguity felt reductive.

On re-reading *Hamlet* with the project in mind, however, I was struck by two things: firstly, how one of Hamlet's central dilemmas — whether to take action or to live forever in his own mind — is crucial for so many young people today; and secondly, how the conception many of us have of ourselves as brooding Hamlet-heroes in our own personal tragedies underlies the individualism of our contemporary world.

This made me think about the offstage lives of the other characters. I realized that, within the elective monarchy of Elizabethan Denmark, people like Laertes might have been infuriated by Hamlet's inherited centrality both in the court and the dramatic action. By giving these supporting players the lead roles we each crave, I thought, and by exploring their reactions to Hamlet's solipsism, I could bring to life the conflicts that an individualistic worldview causes when it is held by everyone in society.

My fears about the reductiveness of writing a prequel were allayed when I saw that another of Hamlet's worries is living up to the role into which he was born — whether he can act as his own agent or is an avenger automated by duty. Addressing this anxiety in a story in which the audience already knows the outcome of the characters' actions would allow me to question the very notion of self-determination, and so give the play a life distinct from its source.

Once I'd agreed on a prequel and a young cast, then, the faux-Elizabethan idiom seemed the only option — these characters would one day speak in Shakespearean English, after all, but as yet would still be green, and so only able to approximate the brilliant later language. After working within the strictures of naturalistic dialogue, it was a real thrill to be able to have characters actually articulate ideas in elaborate rhythms.

Most of all, though, what excited me about Anthony's proposal was the opportunity to approach a play many think of as oppressively serious in an irreverent, fast-paced, fresh way. I hope the pleasure I had writing it translates to the experience of watching it.

**Michael Lesslie**

SCENE 1

*The underbelly of Elsinore. Early evening*

*Clanging sounds from the forges nearby, the fervour of preparation for war*

*Laertes bursts bitterly on to the stage, quickly followed by Reynaldo, wary and watchful. They both speak in urgent whispers*

**Laertes**  But when was this?
**Reynaldo**  Last night, my lord. And every night for the last ——
**Laertes**  From Hamlet, you say?
**Reynaldo**  My lord, they bear the King's seal. Either his father is sending ——
**Laertes**  But have you read them, Reynaldo? Any of them, have you ——
**Reynaldo**  My lord! My duty to your father ——
**Laertes**  (*firmly*) I said have you read them? This is a matter of state.

*Reynaldo nods*

**Reynaldo**  Poetry, my lord.
**Laertes**  Oh God.
**Reynaldo**  Some dozen lines apiece. Confused, mired in paradox ——
**Laertes**  And her replies?
**Reynaldo**  My lord, she proves elusive.
**Laertes**  This cannot come to good, Reynaldo. I cherish my sister more than the mortal earth, but she is a girl, and as such, she cannot be trusted to vouchsafe her own fortune. As for Hamlet … our army prepares for England and its prince writes verse? No. We do not elevate great ones to have them meddle in our affairs, they are above us to serve

us, gilt pinions to our iron wheels. Should the pinion turn against the teeth that hold it, the whole machine will crack. Bring me my sister. And look you, be secret.

*BANG! Laertes and Reynaldo spin around, drawing swords*

*A bumbling, be-hatted fool, Osric, tumbles on stage*

**Reynaldo**  Who goes there?

**Laertes**  Stand and unfold yourself!

**Osric**  If you desire my formal nomination ——

**Laertes**  ⎱
**Reynaldo** ⎰ *(together)* Osric.

**Osric**  Trepidatious woe, Laertes! Your sister is over-suitored! She spurns my cupidinous epistles with the obstinacy of ——

**Reynaldo**  *(aside)* My lord, I will to your command.

**Laertes**  *(aside)* Be quick. Please.

*Exit Reynaldo*

**Osric**  What's to be done? The fair Ophelia!

**Laertes**  Take heart, my lord. You have land, wit, charm … land …

**Osric**  But not enough! I need not remind you of the promise you've made, Laertes. Thanks to my family, your father is newly lodged in court, servant to the King's brother. One day, you could be steward.

**Laertes**  This is democracy. I could be king.

**Osric**  Not if you betray those who support you. Your tenure in Elsinore is still vulnerable, you know. You promised me her favour.

**Laertes**  And I shall deliver it, I swear. Indeed, I believe that servant there may just now have disclosed to me the source of my sister's disdain.

**Osric**  Disdain?

**Laertes**  Distemper. She is coming here presently. Leave us a while, I will dig her to her depths. Woman's affection runs differently to ours, Osric. It is impractical, chaos in miniature, unmannable 'til it choose to be manned. But Ophelia is a sister first, a girl second. She knows her duty. *(Glancing off stage)* Quick, here she comes. Meet me on the battlements this evening, the first watch, I'll tell all. Now go!

*Osric bows elaborately and hurries off stage*

*As he does, Ophelia hurries on from a separate entrance with Reynaldo following close behind*

**Ophelia** My God, Laertes, was that Osric?

**Laertes** A paean to manhood if I ever saw one.

**Ophelia** A talking mushroom! I never knew a man with such a capacity to repulse and bore at the same time, it's like being tortured with wet fruit. Honestly, I don't understand why you still speak to him.

**Laertes** His father is the richest landowner in Denmark. Were it not for his kindness, we would still be in the city, futureless and ——

**Ophelia** Alive! I am bored, Laertes! Father is established, you have a hope in court, and what do I do? Sew and wait.

**Laertes** You're a lady in waiting. That's your job.

**Ophelia** Anticipation. Hardly a future worth looking forward to.

**Laertes** Our mother would have been proud, Ophelia. To see you here.

*Ophelia hesitates. Laertes smiles*

You look so like her, you know.

*Ophelia looks down. Gently, he strokes her face*

(*Quietly*) How much do you love me, Ophelia?

**Ophelia** I cannot say.

**Laertes** Why not?

**Ophelia** Because love can't be put into words, Laertes.

**Laertes** Not even poetry?

*Ophelia looks up*

It lies in action, then. In loyalty.

*He holds her stare*

Why didn't you tell me? You're my sister.

**Ophelia** I'm me.

**Laertes** Part of a greater whole to which you are subject. Don't be deluded into whorish aperture by a slip of high attention, Ophelia, Hamlet's blood and flesh, same as the rest of us.

**Ophelia** He's a prince.

**Laertes** And we are low! All we have is our name. If you open your legs to this degenerate prince, you'll ruin us all.

**Ophelia** He loves me.

**Laertes** You haven't even spoken to him! You've never been alone in a room!

**Ophelia** Not yet.

*Beat*

**Laertes** When? Tell me.

**Ophelia** There's a play tonight for the Norwegian king. We're going to meet afterwards, by the third watch.

**Laertes** Where?

**Ophelia** In my chamber.

**Laertes** You can't, Ophelia!

**Ophelia** I have to! He's the prince, it's treason if I don't agree.

**Laertes** It's treason if you do, to a father, to a family who loves you.

**Ophelia** Who expect me to wait for the rest of my life? I could be queen.

**Laertes** Are you mad?

**Ophelia** Not a jot. I saw something last night, Laertes. During the entertainments, I stole out of court to take some respite and walked down to the brook.

**Laertes** The brook? Ophelia ——

**Ophelia** There was someone there. In the water, a woman, naked, white as the moon.

**Laertes** She's dead, Ophelia. You have to let go.

**Ophelia** No, listen. I hung back behind the trees, my breath freezing in the air, and … I watched. She was cleaning herself, Laertes. As though she were guilty.

**Laertes** So? It was a drab, what's that got to do with ——

**Ophelia** It was the Queen.

*Beat*

**Laertes**  The Queen was in her chamber last night. I heard Father tell the King.

**Ophelia**  No. I went to her chamber straight afterwards, it was empty.

**Laertes**  But Father swore. Why would he lie?

**Ophelia**  I don't know. He's been confused. I'm worried, Laertes. I have to tell Hamlet.

**Laertes**  Why?

**Ophelia**  What if she hurts herself? If we warn him, he might be grateful. Besides, I can't back out now, I've sent the reply.

*Laertes thinks*

**Laertes**  How does he receive your letters?

**Ophelia**  A servant passes them to one of his friends. Guildenstern, I think.

**Laertes**  Not Rosencrantz?

**Ophelia**  I can't tell. The lanky one.

**Laertes**  Reynaldo, come. I shall write out a letter in Ophelia's hand. Will you deliver it to this Guildenstern?

**Reynaldo**  I shall, my lord.

**Ophelia**  But ——

**Laertes**  You are a girl, Ophelia. You must remember that the cost of your giddy passions is a sacrifice of judgement from which we men are thankfully exempt. You are to meet him outside the castle walls, somewhere you won't be seen.

**Ophelia**  Where?

**Laertes**  The shelter on the cliff.

**Ophelia**  But the winds there are freezing!

**Laertes**  Not if you're wrapped up. You must trust me, Ophelia, for our mother's sake. All I ask is discretion.

*Ophelia nods. Laertes kisses her forehead*

Reynaldo, quick, we don't have much time.

*Laertes hurries off stage*

*Reynaldo starts to follow*

**Ophelia**  Wait.

*Reynaldo turns back*

I asked you not to tell anyone. (*Beat*) Watch him for me, Reynaldo.
**Reynaldo**  Why should I take orders from a girl?
**Ophelia**  Because as a girl I have feminine means of payment. Tell me what he writes, please.

*Reynaldo smiles and bows*

**Reynaldo**  My lady.

*Exeunt*


## Scene 2

*The halls of court. Early evening*

*Hamlet bursts on to the stage, impassioned and furious, followed anxiously by Rosencrantz and Guildenstern*

*Behind them, teams of youths practise ceremonial fencing in preparation for the evening's festivities. One bookish fencer, Horatio, is particularly inept*

**Hamlet**  God's blood, what a fool!
**Guildenstern**  Quiet, my liege!
**Rosencrantz**  My good lord, please! The very walls here are ears ——
**Hamlet**  What a kingdom, so taken with hearing that it forgets how to see! Why are you afraid of him, friends? He's just a man!
**Rosencrantz**  To you, my lord, he may be a man. To Guildenstern and I, he is your father.
**Guildenstern**  The King.

**Rosencrantz** You walk with a freer rein than we do.

**Hamlet** Then let me be its sovereign! Surely each of us has the right to break off our parents' chains, Rosencrantz, be we prince or nobleman or anything else on the earth?

**Rosencrantz** So long as we know the consequences of that break.

**Guildenstern** In your case, sire, Wittenberg.

**Hamlet** Go to! My father won't send me away, my mother wouldn't let him.

**Guildenstern** My lord, I have never seem him so distempered. Your outburst before the court just now was indecorous, to say the least.

**Hamlet** Then perhaps in its ugliness it struck of truth! Decorum is the anaesthetic of our age, Guildenstern, a paint that distorts the thing it coats until every object is unrecognizable as its own being. I meant what I said before the King, and it is right that those who elect him hear of his failings.

**Rosencrantz** But what failings, my lord, has he committed?

**Guildenstern** Look how humbly the Norwegian king bows. Surely such servility signifies honour, not debasement?

**Hamlet** Honour?

**Guildenstern** Did you not see?

**Hamlet** No, Guildenstern, I didn't. For whilst that slave-king of Norway toadied himself to his brother's killer, I could not tear my eyes from the rear of the room, where young Fortinbras, silent, aflame, stood strewing both his uncle's servitude and my father's honour with the same wrathful loathing. My father murdered his on the day I was born, friends. As my mother risked very death to bring me into this world, our king was in another country, winning a bet on which he'd wagered the whole nation's future. All for your honour, Guildenstern. And after he had slain old Fortinbras and set up this substitute Norway in his place, did he return to his country to celebrate with his newborn son and birth-torn queen? No. He continues on to Poland, where thousands more sons and fathers and uncles are made to die for his honour. And now, finally, after more than a decade of war, when even his own old bones rebel against his bellicose command, does he come home? Of course he doesn't. As though Denmark were burning purgatory, he immediately announces a campaign for England, an island of drunks and drabbers so deluded by the sight of their own borders that they think they rule the world, which in fact cares no more for them than the warm beer and cold conversation they produce. Again, all for honour. The more countries my father conquers in the name of today's honour, friends, the more enemies he bequeaths us in the future, enemies like young Fortinbras, charged with the fury of filial vengeance. That's far more dangerous than any impulse for honour.

**Guildenstern** So what would you suggest, my lord?

**Hamlet** That he take a leaf from my uncle's book. Claudius. As much a friend to Denmark as King Hamlet is scourge of the rest of the world. The only man who stayed behind to hold my mother's hand as she screamed for assurance. One who commands the love of the country he lives in, capable of making the whole populace laugh with a single smile. What does foreign victory matter when the people you fight for don't recognize your face, or the sound of your voice? Where was Claudius during last night's warlike entertainments? Walking outside the castle walls, no doubt warming the hearts of people that love him. That, friends, is a true king.

**Rosencrantz** Be careful what you advise, my lord. If your father does send you away, he'll have no choice but to depose you as his most immediate heir and nominate Claudius in your place. Not only will you lose your chance of becoming king, you'll be stuck in Wittenberg.

**Guildenstern** And moreover, we'll be stuck with you.

**Rosencrantz** And Wittenberg is dull! A place for monks and midwives, not princes.

**Guildenstern** Or their noble friends.

**Hamlet** So much the better! Were it not for the fair Ophelia, friends, I would dearly desire such an exile. For in Wittenberg, we may no longer be noble. There we may be taken for what we are, separated from role and royalty. Why, a peasant may approach us and shake our hands as equals, made honest by his ignorance.

**Rosencrantz** I fail to see the attraction.

*Hamlet suddenly yells and runs at Horatio, who backs away, hesitant.*
*Hamlet laughs and turns back to Rosencrantz and Guildenstern*

**Hamlet**  Real life, Rosencrantz! In Wittenberg, this fencer here would
have run me through without a moment's hesitation as though I were
just another man. How can we know what we're capable of when
we're shackled by such general licence? We only discover our true
selves when our whole future lies at stake.

*Enter Reynaldo*

But enough of this, here's matter more compelling. How did she
receive my last poem, Reynaldo? Did she smile when she read it? Or
did she frown? Speak freely, such signs are all a lover may live by.

**Reynaldo**  My lord, I cannot tell. But sure, her haste in writing this
reply suggests a reciprocation of the sentiment laid out therein.

*Reynaldo holds out a letter. Hamlet takes it*

**Hamlet**  Oh, Ophelia! There is our true model of freedom, friends! A
spirit of fire, unbridled by the demands of the world! Pure energy
straining at the body that holds it.

**Reynaldo**  Indeed, my lord.

*Hamlet reads*

**Hamlet**  The cliffs? Why would she want to meet there? The winds
alone might throw us over the edge.

**Reynaldo**  I believe for privacy, my lord.

**Guildenstern**  Oh ho! It seems your virginal target may not be as
innocent as you presumed.

**Hamlet**  Quiet.

**Rosencrantz**  Her family is newly come to court, my lord. You don't
know what sordidness these city girls contain.

**Hamlet**  She is pure, Rosencrantz, I'll wager my life. (*To Reynaldo*)
Tell her I'll meet her wherever she desires.

**Guildenstern**  My lord, you cannot mean it?

**Hamlet**  I can and do.

**Rosencrantz**  But you heard the King. After your outburst in court, he ordered that you be confined to your chamber as soon as the entertainments are done. You'll never be able to escape, let alone to board that servant girl.

**Hamlet**  I had forgotten. Let me think, let me think. (*Getting an idea*) Ah! A troupe of tragedians are playing this afternoon, are they not?

**Guildenstern**  They are, my lord. They've come from the city to perform Dido and Aeneas.

**Hamlet**  I've seen these players before. One of them is my age, the one who plays the prince. Reynaldo, bring him here.

*Exit Reynaldo*

Good friends, I serve a greater master than the King. The heavens have dictated that men be free to love and live in full pleasure of their gifts. Ophelia is one such gift, celestial light fallen to earth, and in the eye of the Lord I am as much man as prince. I will meet her tonight whether my father likes it or not.

*Enter Reynaldo with a Player*

**Hamlet**  How goes it, noble friend?

**Player**  Well, my lord. I'm a little nervous, perhaps.

**Hamlet**  Don't be. The audience you perform for today are courtly, so stunted by decorum they'll clap at your every pause, no matter what you might have said before it. Tell them they're murderers and villains and they'll rise to their feet in rapturous approbation.

**Player**  I wouldn't be so sure, my lord. In the city last week we performed a tale of a husband's murder, and in the middle of the villainous speech, a new widow leapt up in the stalls, white as bone, and proclaimed the play her exact biography. She was arrested on the spot.

**Hamlet**  It doesn't surprise me. True-played fiction is far more incisive than any accusation of fact, for the malleable tale will turn a guilty imagination on itself, thus destroying its last hope of defence. But look you, here's matter more urgent. After the play tonight, would you be willing to perform a further role? It must be secret, do you understand?

**Player**  Sire?

**Hamlet**  The King has ordered that I am to be interred in my chamber after the play. Matters of the heart compel me to defy him. If you consent to my plan, after the performance, I shall visit you in your dressing-chamber on the pretence of congratulation. Then, in secret, we shall exchange clothes, and in my guise you will hurry to my chamber as though I were willingly submitting to imprisonment. Once there, spend the evening as you will, but be sure to try the floorboards. These two loyal friends of mine will stand guard and attest that your footfalls proclaim my presence within, whilst I hurry away to my loving enterprise.

**Guildenstern**  But my lord ——

**Hamlet**  I'll return by cover of dark, when the castle's corridors are all asleep. Forgive the secrecy of my mission, friend, but I cannot tell you more lest I ruin a good lady's name. Do you understand?

**Player**  The role of prince is one I am used to, sire. I will not let you down.

**Hamlet**  Thank you. Now quick, to your rehearsals, lest your absence provoke suspicion.

*Exit the Player*

**Rosencrantz**  My lord, as your servant, I tell you this is unwise.

**Hamlet**  And as your schoolmate I beg you to help. You will conspire with me in my love, will you not, old friends?

*Rosencrantz and Guildenstern exchange glances*

**Guildenstern**  My lord, we shall.

**Hamlet**  But swear it.

**Rosencrantz**  Why do you want us to swear, my lord? We have agreed already.

**Hamlet**  Indulge me.

**Rosencrantz**
**Guildenstern** } (*together*) We swear.

**Hamlet**  A quadruple promise, each on behalf of the other. Now come, let's test this plan further.

*Exit Hamlet, Rosencrantz and Guildenstern*

*Reynaldo watches them go. As he does, Horatio approaches him*

**Horatio**  You were ordered to return that letter minutes ago. But you stayed. You listened.
**Reynaldo**  (*surprised*) So did you, it seems. This is politics, Horatio, not philosophy. Go back to your books.

*Exit Reynaldo*

*Horatio watches him go*


SCENE 3


*The battlements. Night*

*Enter Laertes alone, seething*

**Laertes**  Disguised as a player, he says? So, not content with debasing my sister, with ruining my family and stealing from me the only being precious enough to sustain a belief in the gods, this lecher lord is yet so embarrassed by his lust that he must carry out our humiliation in disguise! As a tawdry player! God's blood, his shame confirms his base intentions! This is no prince, this is a tyrant, one who views his subjects as fairground rides for venal entertainment! If he knew the nobility of soul my mother contained he would weep before he dared whisper to her youthful image, let alone board it, and yet this whore-maker will be king! Taken by the whole nation as the measure of a man! What then will happen to Denmark? I have seen him in court, glowering and mumbling to himself as though his troubles would defy the comprehension of mortal men, and we imitate our monarchs as pets their masters. Thus will Denmark be reduced to a nation of cowards, brooding solipsists so paralysed by soliloquy as to be blind to their social duty. And all for nothing. For convention. Why must this player be king? Why Hamlet and not another? My natural capacities are as strong as his. Stronger, my friends might say. Is it man's duty to accept the future handed down to him, or to arm himself against the will of fate and carve out his own fortune? What would happen, say, if Hamlet were removed from Denmark? If he were to fall from the cliffs this very night? Then the direct succession would be interrupted, and the King's brother would become heir. Claudius, my father's lord. And sure, I have seen that when the presumed line is thus disturbed, men's minds are opened to the true possibility of their limitless election. A meritocracy may be born. Then, who is to say that a peasant could not be king? Who is to say not Laertes? And would Denmark be better off? All for a push! I must act. Hamlet, make your peace. Your audience tonight will pay you handsomely for your player's costume. (*Glancing off stage*) But hold, my tongue, for here comes a weapon in my plan.

*Enter Osric*

**Osric**  Laertes, what news? Did you discover the source of your sister's sang-froid?

**Laertes**  Do you think me honest, Osric?

**Osric**  I think you a gentleman.

**Laertes**  Then my gentility compels me to be abrupt. You have a rival.

**Osric**  A rival?

**Laertes**  One of the players newly come to court, an old passion of my sister's from our city days. In faith, he is a robust man, a fulsome specimen of virility.

**Osric**  Then I am lost!

**Laertes**  Is that all? Is that all you will summon for the love of my sister? Why, I was going to suggest a route to your usurpation of this adulterer, but it seems Ophelia was right. You do lack the stomach of a man.

**Osric**  She said that?

**Laertes**  That was the prelude.

**Osric**  Go on.

**Laertes**  She said that you were a handsome fellow ——

**Osric**  True enough.

**Laertes**  But a coward. A spineless, mewling babe too timid to beg his mother for milk, let alone to defend a young girl's honour. Sure, she said, she would give herself to you in the beat of a heart if she saw proof of the manly fire I assured her raged within. But now I see she was right. I shouldn't have bothered devising our plan at all.

**Osric**  What plan?

**Laertes**  No, it is of no use.

**Osric**  I pray you, Laertes, tell me!

**Laertes**  How can I in good conscience? When I've seen how cheaply you esteem her?

**Osric**  I promise you, I love her more than all the jewels in Denmark! More than all the dirt in my fields!

**Laertes**  Enough to fight for her?

**Osric**  Of course!

**Laertes**  Enough to kill?

**Osric**  Why would I have to kill?

**Laertes**  This player plans to board her tonight, Osric. If he succeeds, all is lost. For, sure, once a woman has tasted of an actor's passion, there is no return.

**Osric**  Then what's to be done?

**Laertes**  My sister thinks you a tadpole. A strapling. What better way to disprove her than with a display of might? Eliminate your rival, Osric.

**Osric**  Eliminate him?

**Laertes**  If you are a man. Listen close. Out of our dear friendship, I have contrived that my sister will meet this lover in a secluded shelter on the cliff. We shall go there tonight, you and I, and lie in wait. When you see him press her innocent flesh, rush forward and with a blood-stilling cry of, "I will protect you!", send this paddling player to his doom. Thus will you in one swoop claim your manhood and my sister's affection.

**Osric**  But what if he sees us, Laertes? What if he turns and fights? I have no skill in combat.

**Laertes**  You have your brain, Osric. And so the element of surprise.

**Osric**  That's true. My brain is a formidable weapon.

**Laertes**  And besides, you have heard of my skill with the rapier?

**Osric**  Who hasn't? You are given out as the light of Denmark.

**Laertes**  Well then. I shall be waiting in the shadows, ready to protect you should any mischance occur.

**Osric**  But this is murder, Laertes. If we're caught, we could be put to death.

**Laertes**  Not if the deed is performed with a noble motivation. And what more noble than protecting an angel from her defilement? You shall profess to the judge that you found her locked in struggle with the amorous youth. She won't contest your claim, it would only serve to dishonour her. Thus you shall become at once hero to the court, creditor to your love, and my dear brother. A crime of impunity, Osric, for my sister's heart. You only have one chance. What do you say?

**Osric**  In faith, I do not know. But sure, Laertes, you are a good friend.

**Laertes**  Then why hesitate further? Go, quick, and get you ready. We shall meet at the cliffs by second watch, when I shall give you further reason for our bloodless endeavour.

*Exit Osric*

So be it. I can no more allow this buffoon to have my sister than I can the carnal prince. And he has a claim on me in court, which his arrest will eradicate. It is not on my conscience. The lives of these lords will clear the way for the country's rightful future, and my own just ascension. If the cost of greatness is others' blood, I am willing to pay. Until tonight.

*Exit Laertes*

SCENE 4

*The halls of court. Night*

*Enter Ophelia and Reynaldo*

**Ophelia** And Laertes knows of this?

**Reynaldo** My lady, I told him of the intended disguise. What more he has planned I cannot gather.

**Ophelia** 'Tis well. My brother is a faithful and a decent friend, and my girlish ignorance demands that I put trust in his more sound judgement. Tell Laertes I will meet Hamlet on the cliffs, as we agreed.

*Exit Reynaldo*

These scheming boys! In such courtly company I don't even trust my own blood. What's to be done? (*She thinks. Getting an idea*) Ah! What ho, Horatio?

*Enter Horatio*

Horatio, you are an honest man, are you not?

**Horatio** As far as this world might allow.

**Ophelia** What think you of Reynaldo, then? Is he to be trusted?

*Horatio hesitates*

**Horatio** He is as trustworthy as any courtier in Denmark, my lady.

**Ophelia** Your hesitation speaks bibles. Any nobleman would have been smooth as ice. You can be relied upon, Horatio, I know it. Will you take an urgent message from me to the Lord Hamlet? But do not write it down, I pray you. It seems that in Denmark words thus made flesh can become executioners to their own authors.

**Horatio** What would you have me say?

**Ophelia**  Tell him to meet me at the same hour, but by the brook under the castle walls. There's a willow there that my mother loved. I shall wait for him under its shade.

*Horatio hesitates*

**Horatio**  Madam, you know that in this election of Hamlet over your own blood, you are risking great misfortune.

**Ophelia**  Good Horatio, if I cannot act on my instinct of love, what kind of a person will I be? My brother says that to live is to carve for oneself. Is life then the preserve of men? No, in such boyish times, we women must be loyal to ourselves before we may be loyal to others. I shall meet with the lord Hamlet, let the consequences fall.

*Trumpets sound off stage*

The play's about to start, we must go in. Oh, I am so nervous, Horatio! What if I disappoint him?

**Horatio**  My lady, I have never seen a more suited pairing.

**Ophelia**  Thank you, honest friend. Now quick, take him the message.

*Exeunt Horatio and Ophelia in separate directions*

### Scene 5

*The court. Night*

*Enter Hamlet and Horatio, conferring*

**Hamlet**  The brook, you say? These changing messages bespeak treachery.

**Horatio**  You must trust me, my lord.

**Hamlet**  Why?

**Horatio**  Because I am a scholar. One whose value is set in his own mind, not a prince's advancement. As my brain is my Elsinore, I have nothing to gain from you but the approval of my own conscience.

**Hamlet**  (*surprised*) No one speaks to me like that.

**Horatio**  The more reason to believe me. But keep this amendment to yourself, my lord. There are others in your company whose interests open them to more promiscuous loyalty.

*Enter Rosencrantz and Guildenstern*

**Guildenstern**  Bookworm! Stop bothering the Prince!

**Rosencrantz**  The audience is returning, my lord, we must take our seats.

**Hamlet**  Is that an order, Rosencrantz?

*Rosencrantz and Guildenstern laugh uproariously*

**Guildenstern**  (*pointing to one side of Hamlet*) I'll sit here, my lord.

**Rosencrantz**  (*pointing to other side*) And I here.

*Trumpets sound*

*Enter Laertes, Osric, Ophelia, Reynaldo, Courtiers and Guards, including Marcellus*

*Marcellus steps forward, militaristic*

**Marcellus**  My lords, ladies and gentlemen, the rulers of Norway, and the King of Denmark!

*Trumpets sound and Marcellus gestures to the audience. All save Hamlet turn and bow, but Hamlet remains upright, looking around at the obsequious nobles. They all straighten and sit*

**Guildenstern**  Such a noble carriage!

**Rosencrantz**  Such a royal bearing!

**Guildenstern** (*whispering*) I take it we continue as planned, my liege?
**Rosencrantz** (*whispering*) You still head for the cliffs?
**Hamlet** I do, good friends. There is no change.
**Rosencrantz** Good. Then on with Pyrrhus!

*With a flourish, warlike music starts up and Players rush on to enact
a cacophonous scene of battle. From their chaos emerges the Player.
The action he describes is acted out on stage*

**Player**              And lo! 'Mid the bowels of Trojan carnage
                        The rugged Pyrrhus, he whose sable arms,
                        Black as his purpose, did the night resemble
                        When he lay couched in th' ominous horse,
                        Hath now this dread and black complexion smeared
                        With heraldry more dismal, head to foot.
                        Now is he total gules, horribly tricked
                        With blood of fathers, mothers, daughters, sons,
                        Baked and impasted with the parching streets
                        That lend a tyrannous and a damned light
                        To their lord's murder; roasted in wrath and fire,
                        And thus o'ersized with coagulate gore,
                        With eyes like carbuncles, the hellish Pyrrhus
                        Old grandsire Priam seeks. Anon he finds him,
                        Striking too short at Greeks. His antique sword,
                        Rebellious to his arm, lies where it falls,
                        Repugnant to command. Unequal matched,
                        Pyrrhus at Priam drives, in rage strikes wide,
                        But with the whiff and wind of his fell sword
                        Th' unnerved father falls.
**Hamlet** Dead?

*The Player freezes. The nobles turn to Hamlet in surprise*

**Rosencrantz** My lord?
**Hamlet** (*quietly, to the Player*) I'm sorry. Go on.

*The Player looks out to the King for approval, then continues*

**Player**              Then senseless Ilium,
                        Seeming to feel this blow, with flaming top
                        Stoops to his base and with a hideous crash
                        Takes prisoner Pyrrhus' ear. For lo, his sword
                        Which was declining on the milky head
                        Of reverend Priam seemed i' th' air to stick.
                        So as a painted tyrant Pyrrhus stood,
                        And like a neutral to his will and matter,
                        Did nothing.
**Rosencrantz** (*whispering*) My lord, you have turned to very bone.
**Hamlet** (*whispering*) To the play, look you!
**Player**              But as we often see against some storm
                        A silence in the heavens, the rack stand still,
                        The bold winds speechless, and the orb below
                        As hush as death, anon the dreadful thunder
                        Doth rend the region, so after Pyrrhus' pause
                        A roused vengeance sets him new a-work
                        And never did the Cyclops' hammers fall
                        On Mars' armour, forged for proof eterne,
                        With less remorse than Pyrrhus' bleeding sword
                        Now falls on Priam.

*Hamlet stands abruptly, unsettled. The Player stops again. Hamlet
starts to back towards the exit*

**Guildenstern** My lord?
**Hamlet** I am sorry. I am shaken by this speech, truly. (*To the Player*)
This is an excellent performance, friend. I will hear its conclusion
later, as we have agreed.

*Exit Hamlet*

*Rosencrantz and Guildenstern glance up to the King and follow*

*The howling cliffs. Night*

*Enter Osric*

**Osric**  Oh, I do not like this plan! And sure, the action of the play
did provoke my spirit in much the same manner as it did the noble
prince. My God, murder? Or coward? Which character do I take?
I confess I have no great devotion to the deed, and yet Laertes hath
given me satisfying reasons. 'Tis but a player gone. Forth, my arm,
he dies.

*Enter Laertes*

**Laertes**  What hour now?
**Osric**  I think it lacks of twelve.
**Laertes**  No, it is gone. They should have been here some time ago.
**Osric**  Perhaps her conscience prevents her departure. Let's go in.
**Laertes**  Be strong, Osric! True nobility lies in self-determination, not
in whimsying yourself to the fortunes of others. This is your only
chance.
**Osric**  Be you near at hand, then. I may miscarry it.
**Laertes**  At your elbow, I. Be brave.
**Osric**  As an ox.
**Reynaldo**  (*off*) My lord ——
**Osric**  Help!
**Laertes**  (*drawing his sword*) Who goes there?

*Enter Reynaldo*

**Reynaldo**  Your servant, my lord.
**Laertes**  What are you doing? I told you to keep guard by the castle
gates!
**Reynaldo**  My lord, so I did.
**Laertes**  And did she leave as I intended?

**Reynaldo**  She did, my lord. But on the way, as though aware of her observer, she bled into the darkness and vanished from my sight.

**Laertes**  When was this?

**Reynaldo**  My lord, an hour past.

**Laertes**  An hour?

**Reynaldo**  That's not all, my lord. As I left, it was given out at court that Prince Hamlet has defied the King's order and stolen out of the castle.

**Laertes**  Hamlet?

**Osric**  What's that to us?

**Laertes**  Nothing. But how came this discovery, Reynaldo?

**Reynaldo**  My lord, I do not know. But the King was incensed. He has dispatched Marcellus and a crowd of guards, they are coming here even now.

**Laertes**  Here?

**Reynaldo**  Directly.

**Laertes**  This coincidence bodes ill, Osric. Our shadowy enterprise will not benefit from such an audience. Reynaldo, head Marcellus off and tell him that you saw Hamlet moving east. Divert his party along the cliff whilst we search for my sister.

**Osric**  But where will we find her?

**Laertes**  By the brook, I'll wager my life. Come, quick!

*Exeunt Laertes and Osric, then exit Reynaldo in a separate direction*

<br>

SCENE 7

*The brook. Night*

*Ophelia sits by a willow staring at the water in the audience below. After a pause, she reaches down to touch her reflection*

**Ophelia**  (*singing quietly*) She is dead and gone, lady,
                    She is dead and gone,

> At her head a grass-green turf,
> And at her heels ——

**Hamlet** (*off*) Ophelia?

*Ophelia jumps*

*Enter Hamlet, disguised as the Player*

It's only me. Don't be afraid.
**Ophelia** I'm not.

*Hamlet smiles awkwardly*

**Hamlet** So. Now we are alone.
**Ophelia** Should I curtsy?

*Hamlet shakes his head. Pause*

**Hamlet** Those poems I sent ——
**Ophelia** They were beautiful.
**Hamlet** They didn't even rhyme.
**Ophelia** I'm here, aren't I?
**Hamlet** I'm the prince. You don't have a choice.
**Ophelia** Yes I do.

*Hamlet smiles*

**Hamlet** Why did you change the meeting place?
**Ophelia** My mother used to come here. Before she died.
**Hamlet** I'm sorry.
**Ophelia** People say she lost her mind. But looking at my father … I think she made the sanest choice she could.

*Hamlet hesitates, then sits down next to Ophelia. Pause*

What happened to you in court, Hamlet?

**Hamlet**  I don't know. That speech … People say that plays are made
to awaken the truths lying dormant in their audience. My father …
I don't know him, Ophelia. He is no more father to me than he is
to one of his conquered subjects. And he is ruining Denmark with
his wars, I know it, I know it in my heart. Watching then my double
stand as Pyrrhus, streaked with blood and raising his righteous sword
above the tyrannical old king, it was as though the gods themselves
had climbed down from Olympus and were charging me to earn my
name of greatness.

**Ophelia**  You think you should usurp your father?

**Hamlet**  No. But then, if I feel it is right, why shouldn't I? Why force
myself to obey these ancient roles, son to father and father to son?

**Ophelia**  It was only a play, Hamlet.

**Hamlet**  One still worth the telling some dozen centuries later. Perhaps
if I am to merit such a permanent commemoration, I must do
something equally terrible. Am I a man or a prince, Ophelia? Pyrrhus,
striking for himself in ancient Troy, or the player performing him,
no more in charge of my own life than a mechanical actor reciting
his lines?

**Ophelia**  What do you feel?

**Hamlet**  Myself! Look at you. You are a servant and a woman, but I
know you have that within which surpasses any role.

**Ophelia**  How?

**Hamlet**  I have seen you smile. It is no more the smile of a girl than
it is of a flower, or a cat, or any other earthly being to which we
may draw comparison. It is the smile of Ophelia alone, irreplicable
as the sun. But then, who's to say that up in that sky, elsewhere in
time, there are not hundreds of other Ophelias and thousands of
other Hamlets each as capable of smiling, or passion, or murder
as we? Look there in the water at your pale reflection. Why is that
Ophelia not as real as you are, staring back at us as though we are
but temporary reflections of her more solid self? Then is our sense
of our own uniqueness as mistaken as an actor's pride in his author's
words, and our actions no more good or bad than the performance
of a play. What then does it matter whether I kill the King?

*They stare at the water*

**Ophelia** (*quietly*) If that were Ophelia, she would be drowned.
**Hamlet** In another story, maybe she is.
**Ophelia** If there are hundreds of Ophelias up in that sky, Hamlet, it doesn't matter to me. Because each one will see the world with her own eyes, and so, to her, all its treasures will be wonderfully unique. What then does the truth matter? Here, in my world, I know that I love you now, and always will. What the reflections of me might feel is of no concern.

*Pause*

**Hamlet** My father wants to send me to Wittenberg.
**Ophelia** What do you want, Hamlet?
**Hamlet** Just you.
**Ophelia** Then take me.

*Hamlet looks up at Ophelia. Gently, they kiss. Hamlet presses her back*

   *Enter Laertes and Osric, aside*

**Laertes** (*aside*) Just in time, Osric! Quick, draw your sword!

*Ophelia hesitates*

**Ophelia** Wait. There's something I have to tell you. Last night, your mother ——

*Osric rushes forward brandishing his sword. Hamlet and Ophelia break apart, startled*

**Osric** Unhand her, slave!
**Ophelia** Osric?
**Osric** Indeed I am Osric, one whose nobility compels him to run this peasant through! Have at you!

*Osric lunges at Hamlet, who ducks out of the way*

**Hamlet**  What are you doing?
**Osric**  My duty, vile player! You are no more fit to board this girl than
I am to clean your hovel of a dressing-chamber!

*Osric lunges again. Again, Hamlet narrowly avoids the blow*

**Hamlet**  Dear God, you fool, don't you recognize me? I am Hamlet
the Dane!

*Osric freezes. He looks at Hamlet for the first time and turns deathly
white*

**Osric**  But … But I thought ——
**Hamlet**  Your thoughts are of little consequence. Give me the rapier.

*Osric immediately surrenders the sword and falls to his knees*

**Laertes**  (*aside*) What? No more?
**Osric**  My lord, I profess I was acting out of duty. Had I but
comprehended that it was Your Royal Highness attempting to
seduce this gentle maid, I would of course have never dared to
intervene.
**Laertes**  (*aside*) So much for love.
**Osric**  Please, my lord, don't report this to the King!
**Hamlet**  Don't worry, treasonable rogue. Just leave us alone, and tell
no one what you have seen.
**Osric**  Thank you, my lord!
**Laertes**  (*aside*) This cannot stand.

*Laertes rushes forward*

Is that all?
**Ophelia**  Laertes?
**Hamlet**  It seems this brook isn't as secluded as we may have hoped.
**Laertes**  Osric, for shame! He is defiling your love!

**Osric**  He is a prince.

**Laertes**  And you are a man! Take charge as one.

**Hamlet**  Who is this, Ophelia?

**Laertes**  I am Laertes, your victim's brother, Hamlet, and one who does not care whether you are a prince or a slave. Your abuse demands that I defend her honour.

**Hamlet**  I do not seek to ruin it, noble youth. I love her.

**Laertes**  I love her! More than any prince could ever love! On my brother's authority, I order you to step away from her right now.

**Hamlet**  I care no more for that than the claim of a king. I am as free a man as you, Laertes, there is no authority on earth that can compel me but my own conscience.

**Laertes**  Then it is your conscience I challenge. If you are indeed as free a man as I, fight me for her.

**Hamlet**  Fight you?

**Laertes**  I'll wager your love against mine you won't surpass me in three hits.

**Ophelia**  I am not yours to wager, Laertes.

**Hamlet**  Three?

**Ophelia**  Hamlet, no! He is the most praised swordsman in all the city.

**Hamlet**  What's that to me? I'm undefeated in court.

**Ophelia**  Because no one will let you lose! Please, Hamlet, you don't know your own skill. Don't try to match him.

**Laertes**  Come, Hamlet. Are you a royal coward or a real Dane?

*Hamlet looks between them, then down at Osric's sword*

**Hamlet**  I accept.

**Ophelia**  No!

**Hamlet**  I must stand for you myself, Ophelia. As a man, not a prince. Otherwise how can I know if I deserve you?

**Laertes**  You'll surrender her if I win?

**Hamlet**  And if I do, you'll leave us alone.

**Ophelia**  But ——

**Laertes**  Swear it.

**Hamlet**  I swear. (*To Osric*) You will play the judge?

**Osric**  I shall, my lord.
**Hamlet**  Then come. The best of three hits.
**Laertes**  Let us play!
**Ophelia**  No!

*They raise their swords and start to fight. Eventually, Laertes hits Hamlet*

**Laertes**  One!
**Hamlet**  No!
**Laertes**  Judgement?
**Osric**  A hit, I do declare it!
**Hamlet**  Again!
**Ophelia**  Hamlet ——

*They fight. Hamlet hits Laertes*

**Hamlet**  Mine?
**Laertes**  It is true, I do confess it. Come then, Hamlet, let's play the last. For my sister's love!

*They fight. Laertes gains the upper hand*

*As he does so, Marcellus, Horatio, Rosencrantz, Guildenstern, Reynaldo and Guards burst on stage*

**Marcellus**  Put up your sword!
**Hamlet**  Good fellows, leave him be! He tries a wager to which I have sworn.
**Marcellus**  We cannot, my lord. Your father insists that you come with us immediately.
**Hamlet**  My father? How does he know I've gone?
**Rosencrantz** } *(together)* { I don't know.
**Guildenstern** }              { I've no idea.
**Marcellus**  He is incensed, my lord.
**Laertes**  Will you back out now?
**Hamlet**  Let us play out this bout, Marcellus. Please.

**Marcellus**  My lord, I cannot. These swords are unprotected.
**Hamlet**  Then the greater the victor's honour. Come Laertes, let us play!

*They fight, dodging the Guards that try to stop them. In the midst of the chaos, Laertes trips Hamlet, takes his sword and levels it at his throat. The Guards all freeze*

**Laertes**  Hold off, all of you!

*The Guards stand back, hesitant. Hamlet and Laertes stare at each other, breathing heavily*

You agree to the terms? You will abandon her?

*Hamlet looks from Ophelia to Laertes, caught. He nods*

**Hamlet**  Put up your sword.

*Laertes does. Hamlet stands*

Hold him, Marcellus.

*Marcellus rushes forward and takes hold of Laertes*

**Laertes**  What are you doing?
**Hamlet**  Oaths stand between equals, Laertes. Your courtier's terms can't hold me.
**Laertes**  But you swore! As a man, you ——
**Hamlet**  I am no man, I am the Prince of Denmark! I may do as I please!
**Laertes**  You lying dog!

*Laertes breaks free from Marcellus and rushes at Hamlet*

**Hamlet**  Help, treason!

*Immediately, Horatio rushes forward and knocks Laertes to the ground.
The others catch up and restrain him*

**Laertes** (*struggling*) But he swore! An oath on his honour, a betrayal
before God! Are you going to let this stand, friends? This is tyranny!
The tyranny of his father and his father before him! Of men who
care for nothing but the preservation of their own power! Why
must we live as dogs to such false masters? I say, no more! If we
act together, now, we can end it all. All of you who want to live as
free men, I order you as your fellow to stand back and let me take
my rightful action!
**Hamlet** And as your lord, I order you to hold him fast.

*The Courtiers look between them. No one moves*

**Laertes** Come, friends. Are we such cowards?
**Hamlet** No. You are subjects. Take him in.
**Marcellus** My lord, please, you must come too. The King has
ordered that you go to your chamber immediately and prepare for
Wittenberg.
**Ophelia** Wittenberg?
**Hamlet** I'll lead the way. Do not report this youth's actions to the King,
he cannot be blamed.
**Ophelia** Hamlet?

*Hamlet turns*

**Hamlet** I am sorry, Ophelia. It seems that some authorities have reason
to be upheld. I am the prince, still. Will you wait for me?
**Ophelia** Do I have a choice?
**Hamlet** That depends. Who do you serve? Onwards, loyal Danes.

*Exeunt all but Ophelia and Horatio*

**Ophelia** Good God, Horatio. What's to be done? I pray that none of
these men are ever king.

**Horatio**  Perhaps your wish will come true. Who knows what story
lies in wait?

*Cannons sound off stage*

Young Fortinbras departs. Let's go in. For my own part, I can say that
whoever comes to power, there shall be no escape from bloodshed.
For when human rivalries are thus laid down, private tempers wreak
havoc upon the earth, though all public reasons give them pause. The
rest, Ophelia, is always violence. Come, let's follow the Prince.

*Exeunt as cannons boom out to silence*

FINIS

# FURNITURE AND PROPERTY LIST

*Personal*:   **Laertes**: sword
              **Reynaldo**: sword

*On stage*:   Fencing swords (for **Horatio** and others)

*Off stage*:  Letter (**Reynaldo**)

Nil required

Nil required

Nil required

*Personal*:   **Laertes**: sword

*Personal*:   **Osric**: sword
              **Laertes**: sword

# LIGHTING PLOT

*No cues*

# EFFECTS PLOT

## WEAPONS USED IN THEATRE PRODUCTIONS

With regards to the rules and regulations of weapons used in theatre productions, we recommend that you read the Entertainment Information Sheet No. 20 (Health and Safety Executive).

This information sheet is one of a series produced in consultation with the Joint Advisory Committee for Broadcasting and the Performing Arts. It gives guidance on the management of weapons that are part of a production, including replicas.

This sheet may be downloaded from: www.hse.gov.uk. Alternatively, you can contact HSE Books, PO Box 1999, Sudbury, Suffolk, CO10 2WA Tel: 01787 881165 Fax: 01787 313995.

Lightning Source UK Ltd.
Milton Keynes UK
UKHW020634200920
370211UK00007B/384